MW00395674

This scrapbook has numbered pages. Eac.
15-16 pages plus a pocket (there are five pockets).
Look through the whole book before you start making
it your own, one-of-a-kind scrapbook. And when you do
start, skip around all you want. Write on lines and use
blank spaces for pictures . . . or do just the opposite!
You can draw pictures on any kind of paper and paste
the pictures, or color photocopies on the scrapbook
pages. It's fun to make teeny photocopies, too. Color
pencils, pale felt markers, and ball-point pens work
really well — dark colors soak through. Make funny
combination pictures by cutting out and pasting stuff in
your scrapbook. Have fun!

BLUE DOG

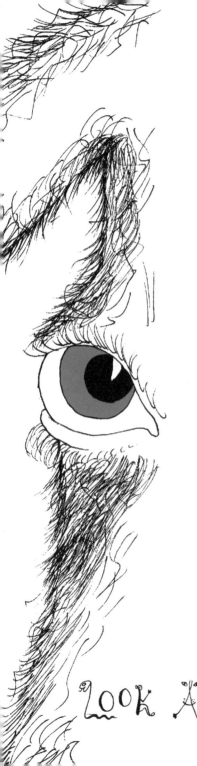

LOOK At These Tweeters, Neighers, Chirpers

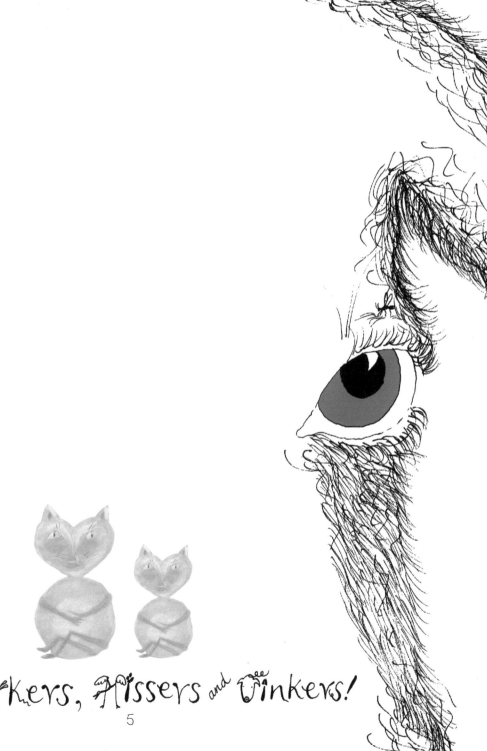

Meowers, Borkers, Hissers and Winkers!

WILD & WONDERFUL

Animal Pictures

An
Animal
Poem or
Story

HEY! YOU ALL—
WHY NOT?
A SONG?

9

in the beg in ning,

10

Nature Pictures

13

The Daily Mews

PURRFECT EVERY DAY ...   ... PAWS AND READ

"ID TALK A
MEOW FOR
ONE OF
YOUR SMIL

The picture above is

14

This picture is

Wowser! In this picture you see

Top dog

Prints

My Friends in Teeny Pictures

me

19

FANCY
FINGERNAIL

MY
HAND
TRACED TODAY

FANCY
FINGERNAILS

____'s
HAND ____ TRACED ON
____ 21

WHAT YOU'D HEAR AROUND OUR TABLE
(DRAW OR PASTE ON THE HEADS, AND WRITE IN THE WORDS)

THIS IS _____

THIS IS _____

THIS IS _____

WHAT YOU'D EAT AT OUR TABLE
(DRAW OR PASTE FOOD PICTURES ON THE DISHES)

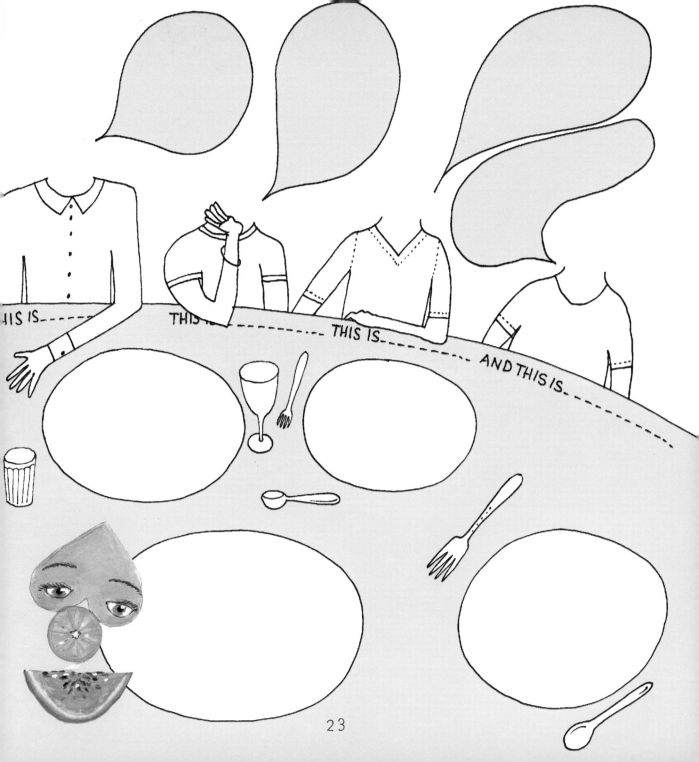

People

Pictures

THE PICTURE

A REALLY GOOD DREAM

The End ??

ALWAYS

OUR DEAR FRIEND

28

Funny Sayings
and family

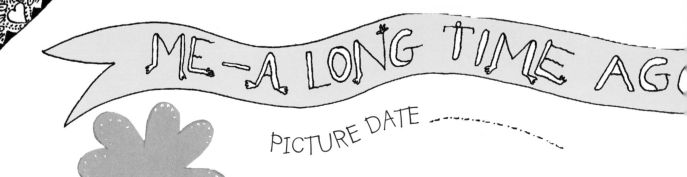

ME--A LONG TIME AGO

PICTURE DATE

and HERE I AM TODAY!

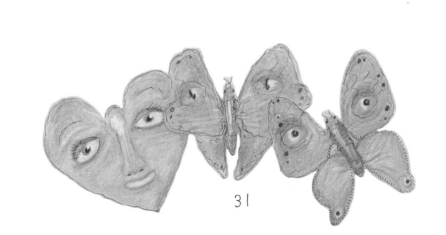

31

My Wish Room

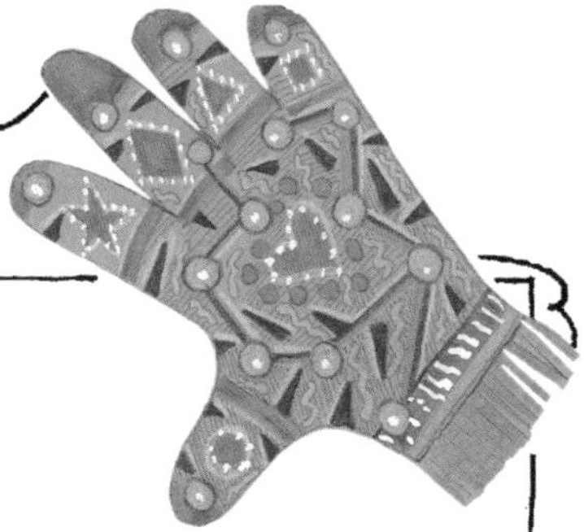

7 GOTTA-HAVES 4 MY ROOM

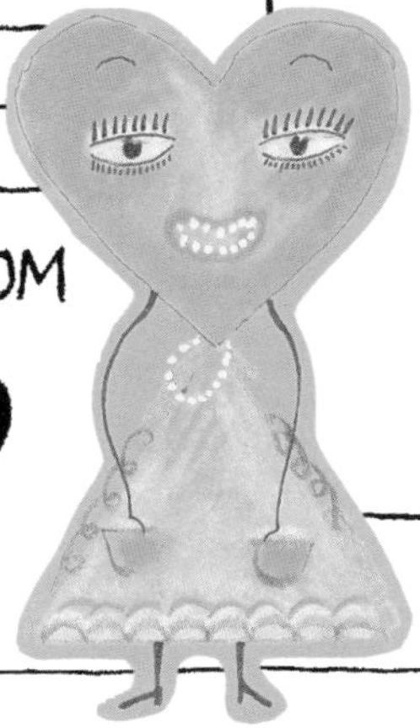

Colors I'd Like

A Really Great Bed

What I wish I had in my room

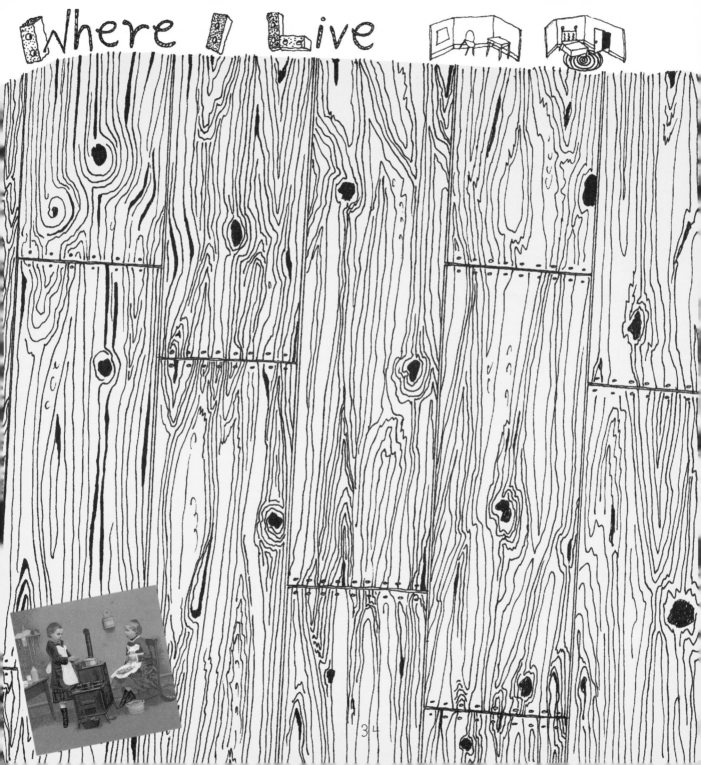

34

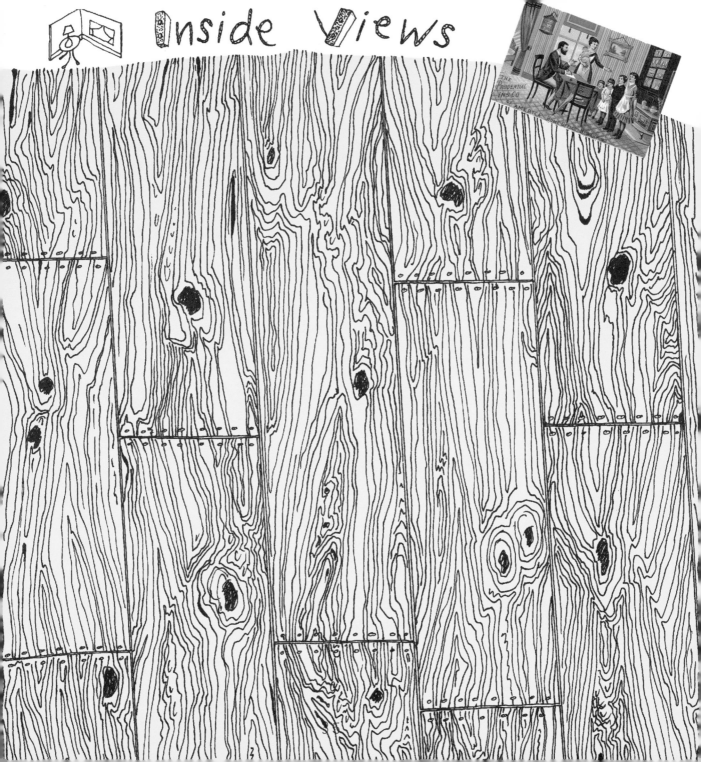

Pictures of WHERE I LIVE

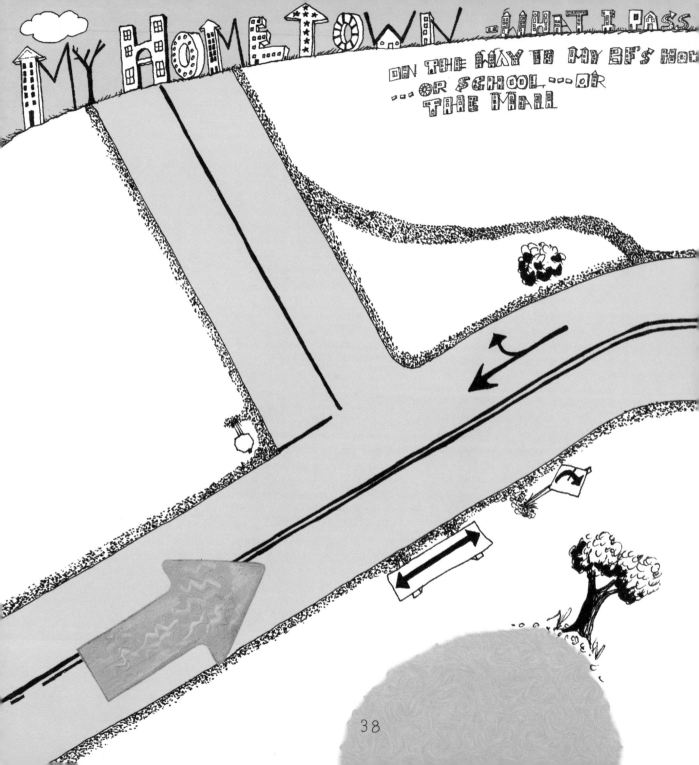

School Views

Home Room: What a ___ Place!

A Dust-Ball Creature

a Dust Bunny

A Picture of A VERY IMPORTANT PLACE

My feelings about A VERY IMPORTANT Place

POST CARDS from ANYWHERE!

ONE MORE SPECIAL PLACE
WHERE WE GO

ONE MORE SPECIAL PLACE

WHERE WE GO

IT'S A : ♡ CAVE ♡CREEK ♡ WOODS   ♡HOSPITAL ♡ KENNEL ☐MUSEUM
♡ GYM ♡THEATER ♡SKATING RINK ♡SPORTS ARENA ♡STABLE ♡DANCE CLAS
♡ LIBRARY ♡CHURCH/SYNAGOGUE ♡STORE ♡FRIEND'S ROOM ♡_____

Where can you go

stay

safe place

MY FAVORITE BOOKS

LEAVE ROOM FOR SOME BOOKS YOU'LL READ THIS YEAR OR NEXT!
THEN NUMBER THEM ⌒ 1 FOR BEST DOWN TO 27

FaVORiTE CDs oR TaPes ♪:

_____
_____
_____
_____
_____
_____
_____
_____
_____
_____
_____

FaVORiTE MUSICIANS

♫♪ MUSIC IN PICTURES

MaKe UP a SONG ♪:

WRITTEN ON_____

FAVORITE TV SHOWS

_____
_____
_____
_____
_____
_____
_____
_____
_____
_____
_____
_____
_____

FAVORITE TV PEOPLE

everything

2 2 MUCH

make up your own show

HEY! WHAT ABOUT YOUR FAVORITE RADIO STATION OR SHOW!

_____
_____

Make Up a Sandwich
Start with a bun or bread
and draw each layer

My Sandwich's Name _____

☐ GOOD 4 A KID ☐ GOOD 4 A TEEN ☐ GOOD 4 A DULT ☐ GOOD 4 A DOG

Sesame Seed Bun
Mayonnaise
Vegetarian Bacon
Lettuce
Banana Slices
Chunky Peanut Butter
Bottom of a Bagel

Potato Chips

or a dirtwich
mais oui?

where are the veggies?

FAVE FOODS
(use words or pictures)

Oh, Right.

Breakfast.

Lunch.

BUT...YUCK

BUT...GROSS

Dinner or Supper.

Snacks.

BUT NEVER

BUT...EEUUW

U R what u eat!

PARTY TIME

Draw or collage
(with magazine
cut-out pix and
paste) a Dress-up
outfit

Describe the
details:

_____
_____
_____
_____
_____
_____
_____
_____
_____
_____
_____

My Favorite
Colors

SCHOOL TIME

Draw or
collage
what you'd
like 2 wear
2 school!

Describe
The Details:

new motto:

My school
Colors

A new
Insignia

55

COLLECTING STUFF

I Like to collect _____

_____

We go to these places to look for stuff: _____

_____

_____

How I got started: _____

_____

_____

Others among my family and friends
also collect! _____ collects

_____ collects _____

_____ collects _____

_____

_____

The best thing I have is _____

_____

SOME PICTURES OF STUFF

Gnu Words from the Dictionary

(WHEN U FIND A NEW WORD THAT U LIKE, USE IT! USE IT OR LOSE IT!)

_____ MEANS _____

_____ MEANS _____

_____ MEANS _____

_____ MEANS _____

_____ MEANS _____

_____ MEANS _____

_____ MEANS _____

_____ MEANS _____

_____ MEANS _____

_____ MEANS _____

_____ MEANS _____

_____ MEANS _____

when you read the dictionary for fun you always find words
that have really useful meanings or really fun sounds — like
NUGGET, HIGH-JINKS, PETTIFOG, SPURT, BUFFLEHEAD, and PEEPUL!

Make Up Secret Words

(U AND YOUR FRIENDS CAN HAVE TOTALLY SECRET PHONE CONVERSATIONS, OR HAVE SPECIAL "SLANG")

(use a pencil)

_____ WILL MEAN _____
_____ WILL MEAN _____
_____ WILL MEAN _____
_____ WILL MEAN _____
_____ WILL MEAN _____
_____ WILL MEAN _____
_____ WILL MEAN _____
_____ WILL MEAN _____
_____ WILL MEAN _____
_____ WILL MEAN _____
_____ WILL MEAN _____
_____ WILL MEAN _____
_____ WILL MEAN _____
_____ WILL MEAN _____

NICKNAMES TOO

ME *
  *
  *
  *
  *
  *
  *
  *
  *

(NICKNAMES AREN'T FOR "NAME-CALLING")

♡ ☆ ♡ ☆ ♡ ☆ ♡ ☆ ♡ ☆ ♡ ☆ ♡

*
*
*
*
*
*
*
*

(WHEN IN DOUBT, ERASE IT OUT)

a Thing Alphabet and a Z

You can make letters in the shape of things (like the chair-h) or make a picture of a thing that begins with each letter, or just make a pretty A - Z.

A a	B b	C c	D d
E e	F f	G g	H h
I i	J j	K k	L l

60

M M
m

N n
n

O o
o

P p
p

Q Q
q

R r
r

S s
s

T t
t

U u
u

V v
v

W W
w w

X x
x

Y Y y
y

Z z
z

2

2

Happiness is Solving Problems.

MY BIGGEST PROBLEM IS _____

_____

_____

AND MY INVENTION TO SOLVE IT LOOKS LIKE THIS!

HUGGING MACHINE · ROOM CLEANER · BRAIN BOOSTER

SEAL OF ORIGINALITY

INVENTOR'S NAME

DATE _____

THIS IS A _____

Design a Tee-Shirt

63

A Valentine for

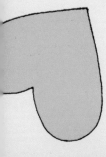

REMEMBER VALENTINE'S
DAY IN _____

MY BIRTHDAY

Date : _____
Year : _____
My age : _____

My Birthday Story

_____
_____
_____
_____
_____
_____
_____
_____
_____
_____
_____
_____
_____
_____
_____
_____
_____
_____
_____
_____
_____
_____
_____
_____
_____
_____
_____
_____
_____
_____
_____

My Birthday Food

_____
_____
_____
_____
_____
_____
_____
_____
_____
_____
_____
_____
_____
_____
_____
_____

Yummy

For a place to keep your birthday cards or a list of your presents, take the biggest envelope (up to 7½" square), turn it upside down and paste the back flap down here in this triangle. Or use this page for photos or scraps of wrapping paper.

OTHER PEOPLE'S BIRTHDAYS

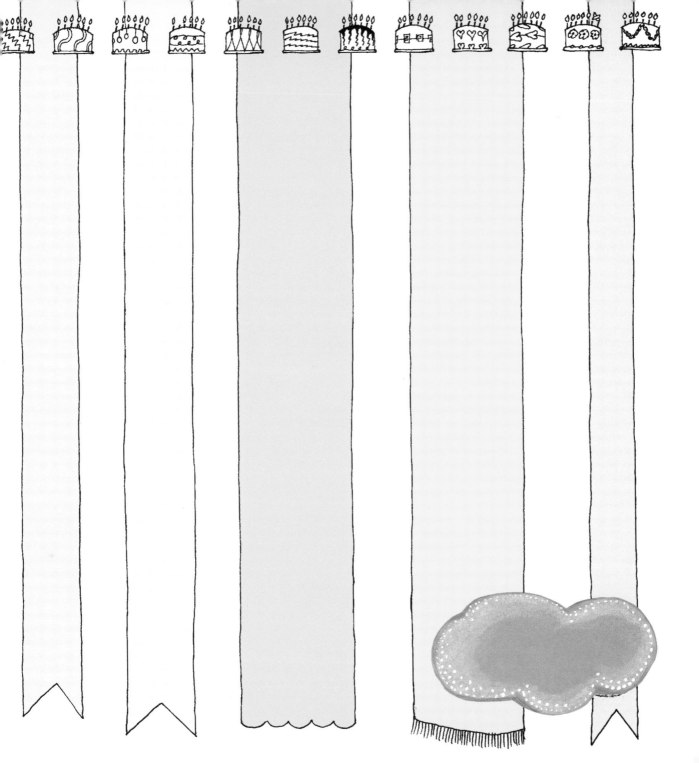

FAVORITE HOLIDAY OF ALL . . .

WORDS AND PICTURES BY ME

School Events

Stick in pictures & tickets & . . .

SCHOOL PLAY

BOOK FAIR

DANCE SCHOOL

PARENTS' DAY

RECITAL

AN THE DAY VISITED ALLIGATOR FOR

DAY BEFORE

SCHOOL LETS OUT

ART EXHIBIT

JEANS DAY

TALENT SHOW

EARTH DAY

PARTY FOR TEACHER

CONCERT

FIRST
HOME
GAME

OPEN HOUSE

GRADUATION

MUSEUM
TRIP

ASSEMBLY

AWARD
DAY

PET DAY

SPELING BEE

SHOW & TELL

LEAP
DAY

BAND

PAGEANT

INTRAMURALS

CLASS TRIP

PLANT A TREE DAY

A VERY IMPORTANT DAY

77

I GIVE A+ TO EVERYTHING

ON THESE 2 PAGES!

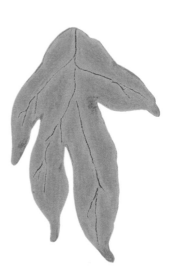

P.S. I want to _____

PLANS

PROMISES

WISHES

WANTS

IDEAS

HOPES

PRAYERS

Yours sincerely

The Whole Family Will Love It!
OCCASIONS
PRIZE!
Good Times
birthdays
Reward
the holidays
Healthy New Year!
big party
Happy birthday